Rob

VENOMOUS ANIMALS

GALLERY BOOKS
An Imprint of W. H. Smith Publishers Inc.
112 Madison Avenue
New York City 10016

This edition first published in U.S.
in 1990 by Gallery Books,
an imprint of W.H. Smith Publishers, Inc.
112 Madison Avenue, New York, New York 10016

ISBN 0-8317-9590-5

Printed and bound in Spain

For rights information about the photographs in
this book please contact:

The Image Bank
111 Fifth Avenue, New York, NY 10003

Producer: Solomon M. Skolnick
Author: Scott Weidensaul
Design Concept: Lesley Ehlers
Designer: Ann-Louise Lipman
Editor: Joan E. Ratajack
Production: Valerie Zars
Photo Researcher: Edward Douglas
Assistant Photo Researcher: Robert V. Hale
Editorial Assistant: Carol Raguso

Title page: The bullet ant, *Paraponera*, packs one of the most potent stings in the American tropics. About an inch long, this insect's powerful venom can cause a loss of consciousness in humans. *Opposite:* Beautiful but deadly – although only to invertebrates and small fish – a cluster of sea anemones wave their tentacles in the currents on a coral reef. Anemones may look like plants, but they are sedentary animals related to the corals, and use stinging nematocysts in their tentacles to kill their prey.

Here's a puzzle. In the jungles of Central and South America lives a tiny frog, a little bigger than the last joint of a man's finger. It is a pretty creature, with a brilliant crimson body and dark blue legs – innocuous enough to look at.

But pick it up by a leg, and the frog struggles. From its back a milky-white fluid is secreted. On the human skin it is harmless, but should you touch a finger to your mouth, or carelessly rub your eyes, or get it in a cut, the mistake could be deadly – for the secretion from the skin of a dart-poison frog is an amazingly strong toxin. In the days before firearms, the Cholo Indians of Colombia tipped their blowgun darts and arrows with the poison. A single frog was said to produce enough to treat 50 darts, each capable of killing a victim.

Why does a tiny frog need such a virulent defense? When the topic is venomous animals, nature is full of such questions. Why is it that the venom of the American house spider causes only a mild, bug-bite reaction in humans, while that of the closely related black widow can cause wrenching convulsions, even death? And why does a spider need venom that kills large mammals, when its normal prey are tiny insects? So far, no one knows.

This page, top to bottom: Two *Percula* clownfish hover among the tentacles of a large anemone, immune to its sting. Unlike the clownfish, most reef fish are killed by contact with an anemone's sting; here, an orange ball anemone draws a dead fish into its mouth for digestion. A giant green anemone partially inverts its digestive cavity around a fish that it has killed.

The striated cone shell of the south Pacific, which belongs to one of the most dangerous families of invertebrates in the world, is pretty enough to tempt divers and beachcombers but packs a barbed stinger armed with venom that can easily kill a person. *Right:* A textile cone glides across a coral head, searching for small fish that it will kill with its venom and then eat. The textile cone is the most poisonous of the 400 cone shell species, and is responsible for most of the human deaths attributed to the family.

Common on the reefs off Florida and in the Caribbean, fire coral causes a painful, burning rash if it is touched, but the stings are not dangerous unless the victim is allergic to the venom. *Left:* The aptly named crown-of-thorns starfish of the Pacific is one of the few poisonous sea stars in the world; the danger to humans comes from handling the prickly creature and breaking off a spine under the skin. *Opposite:* Dangerous enough in their own right, the protective spines of some sea urchins also contain venomous glands that cause intense, long-lasting pain should a diver be foolish enough to handle or step on them. This well-armed example is the black-spined sea urchin.

These pages: Lovely in its extravagance, the lionfish (also known as the turkeyfish or zebrafish) is a common reef species in the Red Sea and Indo-Pacific region. The long dorsal and pectoral frills conceal venomous spines that the fish uses for defense when provoked; lionfish are so docile, however, that they are favorites with marine aquarists.

The mysteries – and the danger – add to the allure of venomous animals. Almost every class of animals has a few in its ranks – venomous fish and insects, toads and snakes and lizards, beetles and spiders and wasps, a whole host of jellyfish, coral, and hydroids. There are even a few venomous mammals, like the short-tailed shrew and the duck-billed platypus. In fact, the only group of strictly non-poisonous vertebrates are the birds.

It is important to understand the terms "venomous" and "poison-ous" which are often used inter-changeably. In a strict sense, venomous refers to animals that produce toxin that is meant to be injected, through a fang, stinger, or spine; a poisonous animal is one that produces toxins but lacks a method of envenomation. Examples of the latter include the frogs and toads, as well as fish with poisonous flesh, like many of the tropical pufferfish.

Preceding page: **Mouth wide, a moray eel looks far more dangerous than it is. Long accused of being poisonous, the many species of tropical morays are in truth virtually harmless – capable of a nasty bite if provoked, but by nature shy and retiring, as well as nonvenomous.** *This page, top to bottom:* **This well-camouflaged fish rests off Baja California. A three-spined scorpionfish blends with its surroundings in a coral reef cranny, where its innocent appearance belies the fact that it packs a potentially deadly wallop of poison. The dorsal spines of another species are held erect when the fish is threatened; should a person step on it, the venom glands near the tips of its spines release the poison, which can cause paralysis, coma, and death.**

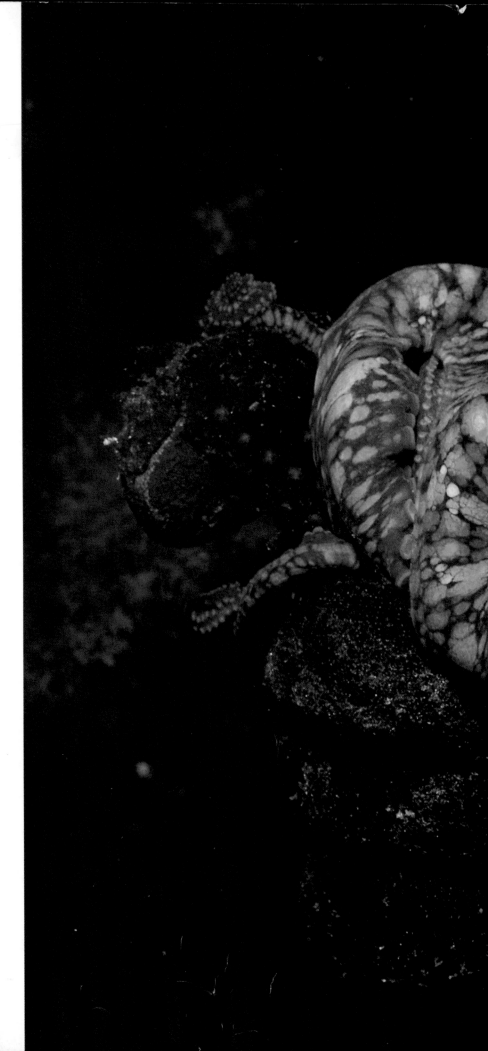

Each group of venomous animals has its own kinds of toxins, methods of envenomation, and uses for poison. Some animals have rudimentary envenomation systems – the Gila monster has grooved teeth that permit the venom to trickle into a ragged bite – while others are remarkably sophisticated. This is especially true of many of the so-called "lower animals." Jellyfish, which are among the most primitive of multi-celled organisms, have tentacles covered with nematocysts, almost microscopic capsules in the outermost layer of skin. When a trigger bristle brushes against an intruding object, a tightly coiled, sharply pointed tube springs out of the nematocyst, piercing the object and injecting venom. A jellyfish sting that leaves a red welt across a swimmer's leg is actually the result of thousands of individual nematocysts, each unloading their tiny bit of venom. The result may be an unpleasant itch, a painful burning or – in the case of the sea wasps and box jellies of Australia – death.

Although they belong to different classes, jellyfish, corals, and sea anemones all use nematocysts to gather food and protect themselves. Jellyfish are ethereal – usually translucent, drifting gracefully on the currents below the water's surface with their tentacles

Like spiders, all octopi apparently produce venom for food-gathering, but only a handful of species pose a threat to people. This harmless species is a Pacific octopus, off the coast of California. *Following pages:* Often referred to as the most poisonous animal on Earth, the lovely blue-ringed octopus of Australia has venom that can kill a person in less than two hours. A tidal-pool animal, the blue-ringed octopus has no fangs, but simply squirts venom into the wounds caused by its small, sharp beak.

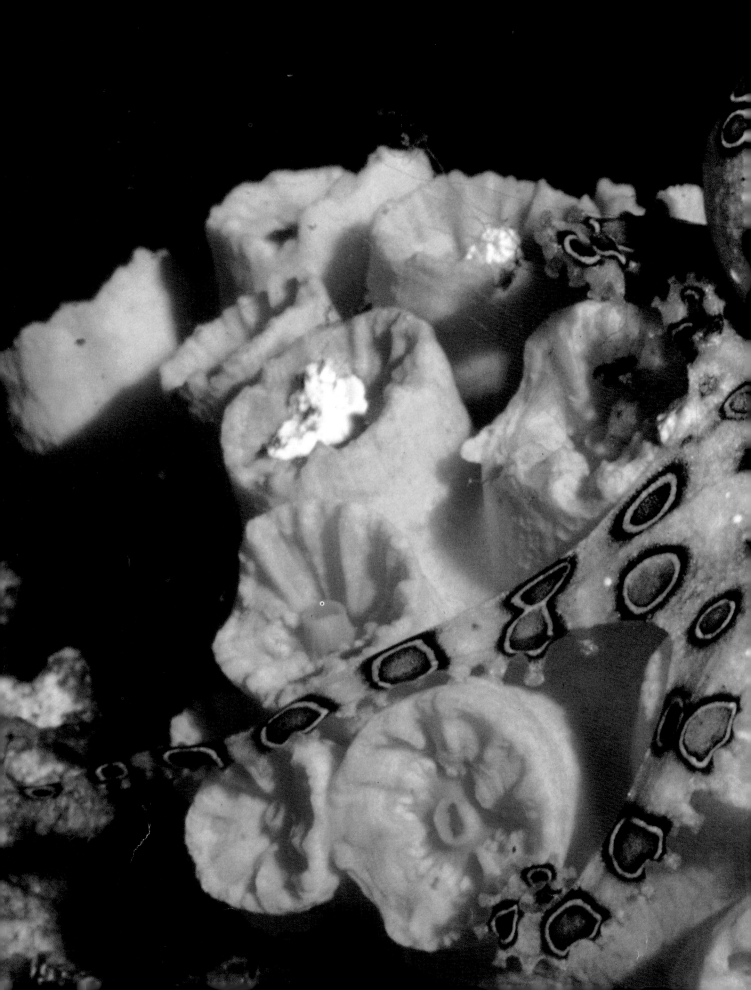

A cuttlefish glides gracefully through the coral off Papua, New Guinea. Octopi, cuttlefish, and other cephalopods produce a venom known as cephalotoxin that allows them to immobilize their prey. *Below:* In addition to a toxic slime that discourages fish, some nudibranchs have a unique way of protecting themselves – they eat stinging hydroids, absorb the nematocysts, and transfer them to their skin, where they then guard the nudibranch.

The banded sea snake, found from India through the South Pacific Islands, is one of the most common of the world's 50 sea snake species. All are poisonous, and some are considered to have the most toxic venom of any snake. Despite their marine habits, they are air-breathers, just like their terrestrial relatives, the cobras.

trailing behind; most can flap their bells (the umbrella-shaped "body") feebly, but are not capable of purposeful movement. They range in size from the minute to the huge, with the world's largest being the lion's mane jelly, which can develop a bell eight feet across, with tentacles that extend 200 feet or more.

Some jellyfish can injure humans, although serious harm is unusual. The Portuguese man-of-war (not a true jelly, but a colonial hydrozoan) has long been accused of causing human fatalities, and while it does inflict fiery welts, it has not been conclusively shown to be deadly to swimmers. The same cannot be said about the Australian sea wasp, which has been implicated in dozens of deaths. In some cases, the victims died in less than an hour after contact, suggesting a level of toxicity that few other animals can match.

The only important stinging coral is the aptly named fire coral, found in the Caribbean and Red Seas, and all too well-known to divers and snorkelers who have inadvertently brushed up against its orange-y branches. The sting is not dangerous (barring an allergic reaction) but it certainly can ruin a day in the water.

This page, top to bottom: **The poisonous tail barb of this southern stingray juts up and back from the middle of the tail, ready to jab a large predator like a shark—or a swimmer who unwittingly steps on the ray buried under the sand. The spotted eagle ray, here shadowed by a remora, is a more active swimmer. Likewise equipped with a barb is the blue-spotted stingray of the Red Sea.** *Opposite:* **Although primitive animals only slightly more advanced than sponges, jellyfish have a sophisticated envenomation system, in which tiny coiled threads, tipped with barbs and supplied with poison, sting whatever they brush against.**

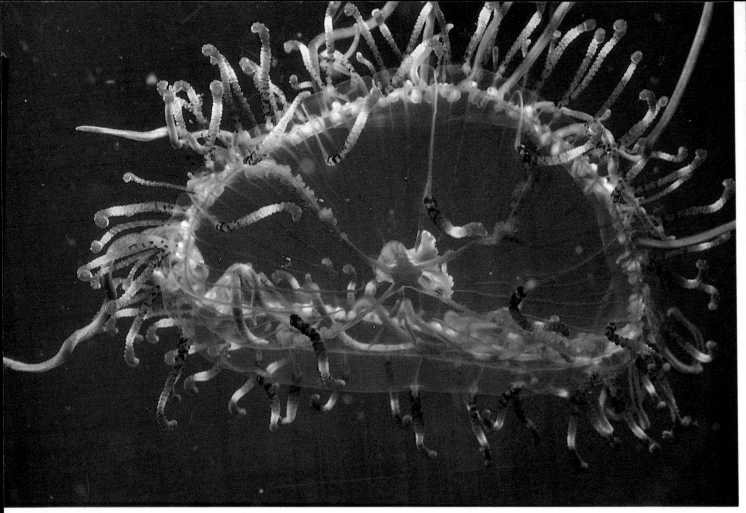

Most jellyfish feed on plankton snared by sticky tentacles and transferred to a central digestive organ. *Below:* The sea wasp is a small jellyfish, usually less than four inches long, but it has a viciously strong sting, and a larger Australian relative has been implicated in the deaths of dozens of swimmers. *Opposite:* Although the tentacles of a jellyfish, like this specimen from the Arctic Ocean, can be deadly for fish, some species routinely live among them, apparently immune to the stings and receiving protection from predators.

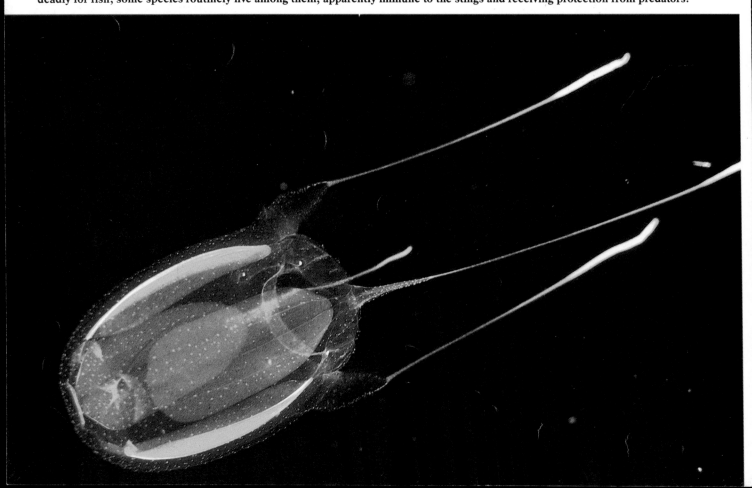

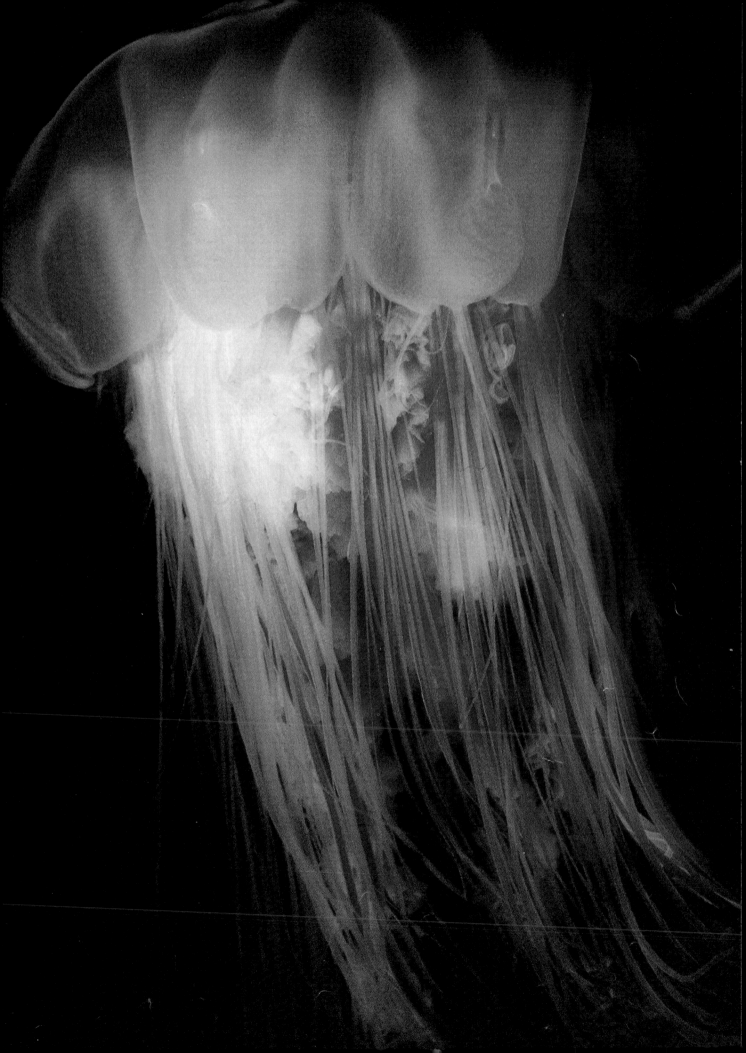

As thousands of people in the Southeastern United States have discovered, the fire ant's sting is painful, and the tiny ants do not hesitate to use their venom to protect their nests. Except to small children and those with an allergy to insect venom, however, the stings are usually not dangerous. *Opposite:* Harvester ants – here carrying plant buds in the Sonoran Desert – are relatives of the fire ant, and like them are members of the subfamily *Myrmicinae,* the stinging ants. The other common North American ant group, the *Formicinae,* do not sting, and include the large, black carpenter ants often found in homes.

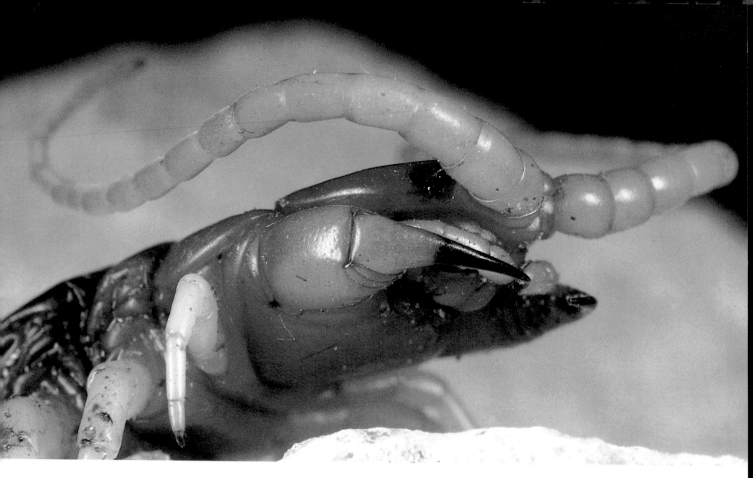

A large centipede in central Texas raises its head, exposing the twin telopodites, or poison appendages, that it uses to catch and kill animals as large as lizards. Such large *Scolopendra* centipedes are rarely dangerous to humans, but their stings can be painful, and tales of fatalities, although unsubstantiated, would counsel caution. *Below:* The giant Mulu centipede photographed in Deer Cave in Borneo, is an exceptionally large example of the family *Scutigeridae,* which includes the much smaller house centipede common in North American homes.

Many species of octopi and cuttlefish have venom, although in most it is weak, with no efficient method of delivery. The spectacular exception is the blue-ringed octopus of Australia, a small, lovely animal that has killed many unsuspecting beachcombers attracted by its electric blue markings.

In terms of human fatalities, the most dangerously venomous animals are not snakes or scorpions, but wasps and bees. The venom of a single honey bee is not usually more than an annoyance to a normal adult – but to a person with an allergy to the proteins in bee venom, the result can be a severe reaction ending in fatal shock.

Bees and wasps are not the same, although people use the terms with little regard for biology. Most wasps (including yellowjackets and hornets) belong to the vespid or sphecid groups; many use their stingers to gather food such as small insects, and sphecid wasps, like the mud-daubers, hunt spiders or caterpillars, which are paralyzed with a sting, sealed in a nest chamber, and left as food for the wasp's grubs. Bees, such as honey bees and bumblebees, use their

Above: **The red hourglass of the black widow spider may be one of the best-known warning symbols in nature – with good reason. The black widow is one of the few truly dangerous spiders in the world, with venom capable of causing muscular cramps, convulsions, and even death.** *Right:* **A female black widow tends to her silk-shrouded egg masses beneath a rock in Zion National Park, Utah. Widows, including the black, brown, and red-legged widows and the red-backed spider, are found over most of the world and account for the majority of human deaths from spider bites.**

venom in a strictly defensive manner, since they feed on plant pollen and nectar. Even the stinger shapes differ between wasps and bees; most wasps have smooth stingers that can be withdrawn from the victim and used again, while honey bees have barbed stingers that remain embedded in the flesh. When the bee pulls away, the stinger, venom gland, and a portion of the bee's digestive system rip loose, dooming the bee. Muscles around the venom gland continue to contract even after separation, pumping more and more venom into the victim's wound.

Venom is widespread among the insects (often in the form of a venomous bite, as with the ambush bugs, or venomous spines in some caterpillars), but it is universal among spiders, serving as both a method of killing food and a means of liquefying it so the spider can drink through its sucking mouth-parts. Only rarely do spiders pose any danger to people, however. Most are not big enough to pierce our relatively thick skin, nor do they possess venom that produces any sickening effect. The exceptions can be dangerous. The group of cobweb spinners called widows are found almost worldwide; in North America the black widow, brown widow, and northern widow are widespread, and the red-backed spider of Australia is especially dangerous. Fortunately the widows are not aggressive spiders, although anyone reaching recklessly into a rock pile, stacked firewood, or beneath an outdoor overhang runs

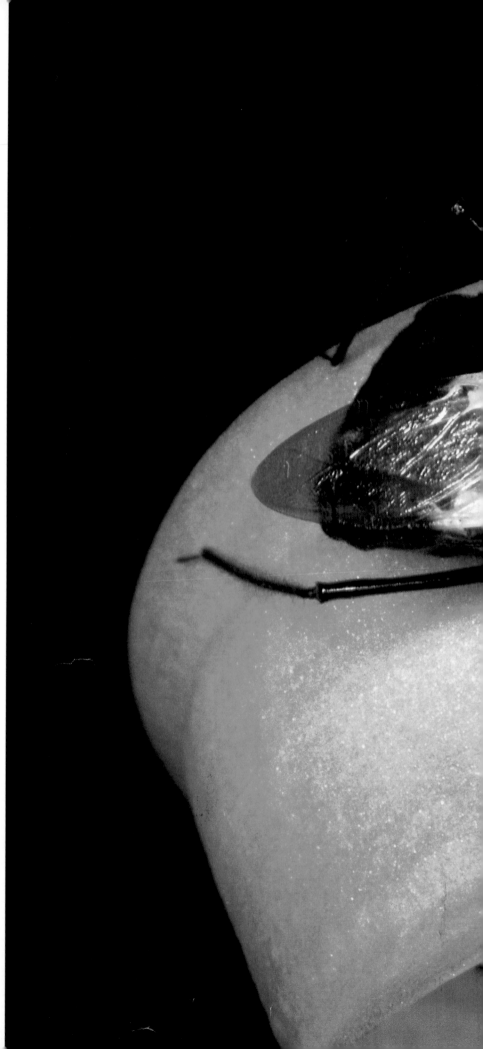

An assassin bug skewers a small bee with its long proboscis, which serves as a venom injector and a feeding tube. Assassin bugs can cause a painful, stinging bite in humans if carelessly handled, and a few species are blood-sucking.

Its oddly shaped thorax gives the wheel bug its name, and probably helps camouflage it among leaves and flowers by breaking up its outline, allowing it to approach other insects. Then the folding mouthpart swings forward and the wheel bug stabs its prey, killing it with a dose of venom. *Below:* If disturbed, many beetles will secrete irritating chemicals, but the blister beetles, like this species from Zambia, produce a substance called cantharidin that can raise blisters on human skin. A number of species are also found in North America.

the risk of disturbing one with disastrous results. The bite produces excruciatingly painful cramps and convulsions, and sometimes death.

Less dangerous, but still cause for worry, is the brown recluse, also known as the fiddlehead spider because of the distinct, violin-shaped marking behind the head. Brown recluse bites can cause painful, lingering lesions, but usually not death, although fatalities are known.

Ironically, the spiders that are most often thought of as deadly—the tarantulas—are no hazard at all, as their recent popularity in the pet trade suggests. Docile unless provoked, these big primitive spiders have rather weak venom, usually compared to a wasp sting in severity. Likewise, scorpions hold a deadly place in folklore, but the stings of most do little more than hurt. There are dangerous exceptions, though, and caution should be used whenever one is in scorpion country—not sticking one's hands in dark nooks and crannies, shaking out boots and clothing in the morning, and not walking in bare feet outside after dark.

A newly hatched giant water bug emerges from its egg, one of many glued to the male's back by the female. Giant water bugs, common in ponds and sluggish streams, are predaceous; the same venom they use for capturing tadpoles and insects makes a water bug's bite painful to humans, as well. *Overleaf:* Worker honey bees crowd around the queen, feeding and cleaning her. Honey bees have a complex social structure, with three castes—the fertile queen; the sterile female workers who collect nectar and pollen, tend the hive, and defend with their stingers against attacks; and the male drones, who exist only to fertilize the queen.

A bumblebee feeds on flower nectar, covering itself with pollen in the process – and insuring cross-pollination when it visits the next blossom. Like honey bees, bumblebees are social insects, although the workers and drones generally die each fall, with only the queen surviving the winter and starting afresh in spring. *Below:* A drone honey bee emerges from its cell after pupating, as worker females tend to the next generation of grubs. *Opposite:* A honey bee gathers pollen on a cosmos flower in a Colorado garden. Probably not native to North America, honey bees are today the most valuable insect on the continent, and their pollination services are essential for agriculture.

Recipient of much unwarranted hype, the Africanized honey bee—the so-called "killer bee"—is nothing more than an especially aggressive strain of the standard honey bee. Its venom is no more dangerous than any other honey bee, but its habit of attacking in large groups makes it more of a threat. *Opposite:* The paper wasps are a widely distributed group in the order *Hymenoptera,* which includes ants, wasps, and bees. Although they will sting if provoked, paper wasps usually reserve their venom for the small insects on which they feed.

The number of venomous fish is relatively low, compared to the number of fish overall, but the percentage of dangerously poisonous species is quite high. The scorpionfish and stonefish head the list. Most are not much to look at — indeed, sitting quietly on the bottom they resemble nothing so much as a sponge-encrusted rock. For protection, the scorpionfish have a series of dorsal spines connected to venom glands; when a larger fish tries to swallow one (or a beachcomber inadvertently steps on one), the scorpionfish's glands rupture and venom squirts into the wound. The level of pain is said to be astounding, and death can follow in minutes. A group of relatives, the lionfish, have dorsal and pectoral spines encased in long, frilly fins that give the fish a lovely appearance. While attractive and popular with aquarium hobbyists, the lionfish can cause a nasty sting if bothered.

Other venomous fish include the stingrays, which have an elaborate spine-and-venom gland apparatus in the tail; the catfish, which have mildly poisonous dorsal and pectoral spines; and the weeverfish of the Mediterranean and coastal Africa, which have killed humans with their venomous dorsal spines.

This page, top to bottom: **A female thread-waisted wasp stings a tent caterpillar — not to kill, but to immobilize it; her grubs will feed on the living, paralyzed caterpillar. Yellow jackets swarm over a rotting apple, attracted by the sweet pulp — the same behavior that makes them unwelcomed guests at picnics. Nocturnal *Polybiin* wasps use their long bodies to cover the open end of their nests in the Peruvian rain forest, shielding the eggs and larvae inside from danger.**

The marine toad, at 12 inches the biggest toad in the New World, is also one of the most poisonous. Wart-like parotoid glands behind the head secrete a milky fluid that makes predators violently ill, and frequently causes death in animals as large as dogs; in Haiti it is an ingredient in the potions that cause voodoo "zombies."
Below: A Colorado River toad ambles along a mud flat, safe from most attackers because of its toxic skin secretions. While effective against most predators, the toxins are useless against some snakes, like the hognosed snake, which specialize in eating toads.

Breathtakingly beautiful, a dart-poison frog's garish colors advertise its presence in the Costa Rican rain forest. The staggeringly powerful skin toxin secreted by the tiny amphibians can kill any creature, including humans, foolish enough to get the secretions in its mouth. *Below:* A California toad's bumpy, granular skin blends well with the rocky background. The toxic skin secretions of the amphibians are strictly defensive, and are not used for capturing prey.

Poison is widespread among the amphibians and reptiles, although it is strictly a passive defense with skin glands secreting the toxin to repel predators. A raccoon that foolishly gobbles down a red-spotted newt will wind up retching and gagging (and the newt may well survive the brief encounter.) Other amphibian toxins are more power-ful. The skin secretion of the tropical marine toad can kill a dog – and potentially a small child that gets the toxin in his or her mouth – but the most powerful poison of all belongs to the afore-mentioned dart-poison frogs of the Neotropics.

Of course, killing an attacker with a deadly poison does the individual frog no good, if in the course of the attack, the frog itself is killed. So most poisonous amphibians' skins are of bright, almost garish hues, known as warning coloration. Far from camouflaging the animal, the pattern stands out like a neon sign that predators can recognize. So effective is warning coloration that many non-poisonous species mimic toxic relatives, thereby crowding under their umbrella of protection.

This page, top to bottom: **One of the most widespread of the dart-poison frogs, *Dendrobates pumilio* is also one of the most variable in color; this Costa Rican specimen shows a common pattern, while others of the same species may be green with yellow legs. Bright colors warn away predators that might be tempted to eat this harlequin tree frog of Central America; thought not as deadly as a dart-poison frog, it has a disagreeably toxic skin secretion. One of the many species of tropical leaf frogs, *Agalychnis callarifer* is only mildly toxic, and so relies on cam-ouflage, rather than warning coloration, for protection against danger.**

Among the lizards, only two close relatives have developed venom – the Gila monster of the American Southwest, and the Mexican beaded lizard. The venom is strong, but the few bites suffered by humans have almost universally been the result of careless handling or horseplay.

To the vast majority of the public, poisonous snakes are the epitome of venomous animals. Few are as dangerous or as aggressive as popular imagination would have it, but the threat is real, especially in poorly developed tropical regions with a high number of venomous species and poor medical care. As late as the 1950's, world deaths from snakebites were estimated at 40,000, with as many as half in India, and while treatments have improved greatly in recent years, the toll is still significant. In the U.S., by contrast, the number of fatal snakebites annually is a dozen or so, a figure that results from few dangerous poisonous snakes and good medical care.

One of only two poisonous lizards in the world, the Gila monster of the American Southwest and northern Mexico is a sluggish, inoffensive animal, and although its venom is powerful, it bites so rarely that it is no real hazard to people. *Left:* A Gila monster raises its head, allowing the contents of a crushed quail egg to run down its throat. The Gila monster and the closely related Mexican beaded lizard feed on eggs, mice, young birds, and rodents, and use their venom only for defense – their crushing jaws are quite sufficient for food-gathering. *Opposite:* In the arid scrublands of southern Africa, a Cape cobra raises itself off the ground in an unmistakable threat. The cobras are elapids, a family that includes the coral snakes and sea snakes, and whose powerful venom destroys the victim's nervous system.

Preceding page: Flexible ribs can expand the hood of this Asian cobra whenever the snake becomes nervous, making it look larger and more dangerous than it would otherwise appear. While many species of cobras are by nature retiring, their habit of living near humans makes them exceedingly dangerous. *This page:* Having killed them with a bite of neurotoxic venom, these king cobras begin the long process of swallowing their prey, other snakes. At more than 18 feet in length, an adult king cobra is the largest poisonous snake in the world.

In an unfortunate case of guilt by association, the harmless banded water snake of the Southeast (above) is often mistaken for the cottonmouth (left), a common pit viper of river banks and swamps. The cottonmouth (also known as the water moccasin) has a distinct, dark band that runs from the eye to the corner of the mouth, which the non-poisonous water snake lacks. *Opposite:* Look closely— this Peringuey's viper is all but invisible, buried as it is in the sands of Africa's Namib Desert. The snake's eyes have a pronounced upward alignment, so the viper can see while it is waiting for prey.

Snake venom is generally of two types – *hemotoxic* venom that attacks the circulatory system, and *neurotoxic* venom that destroys the nervous system. The pit vipers, including rattlesnakes, copperheads, and cottonmouths, as well as Old World adders and vipers, have primarily hemotoxic venom. Once injected through the snake's hollow fangs, the venom begins to dissolve tissue, especially blood vessels and corpuscles; it is a terribly painful experience, often likened to the searing pain of a burn. A lethal dose kills by causing massive internal bleeding and organ damage. Neurotoxins, on the other hand, produce little pain, but interfere with the nervous system, and usually kill by cutting off breathing. This type of venom is found in sea snakes, cobras, kraits, coral snakes, and other elapids. Some poisonous snakes have venom with characteristics of both. The tropical rattlesnake of Central America for instance, has a neurotoxic component in its venom that produces a "broken neck" effect in bite victims by damaging the spinal column, as well as a hemotoxic component which affects other tissue.

Preceding page: Its patience rewarded, a Peringuey's viper prepares to swallow a gecko that it has ambushed and killed. *This page, top to bottom:* The southern copperhead is similar to the more widespread northern copperhead, but its color is paler, and the dark crossbands do not meet along the center of the back. A female northern copperhead, with the characteristic dusky hue, stands guard over her newborn babies; the young will soon be left on their own, for she provides no real care. The Gaboon viper is the most massive venomous snake in Africa – a six-footer can swallow a young antelope, and may have fangs more than two inches long.

The horned viper is another snake adapted to life in the desert—in its case, the Sahara. The unusual hornlike projections probably help direct sand away from the eyes, which are protected beneath clear scales. *Below:* Unusually exposed, a Peringuey's viper (also known as the sand viper) shows its rough-scaled appearance which helps to camouflage the snake in the African desert sands.

Just a baby now, this young bushmaster will grow to be the largest poisonous snake in the Western Hemisphere, with a maximum length of 12 feet. Undoubtedly dangerous, the bushmaster accounts for fewer human fatalities than other Latin American snakes, possibly because it prefers undisturbed jungle rather than farming areas. *Right:* The tree trunk viper — here curled among the leaves of a Sumatran forest — belongs to the Asian pit viper family, which is closely related to the pit vipers of North and South America.

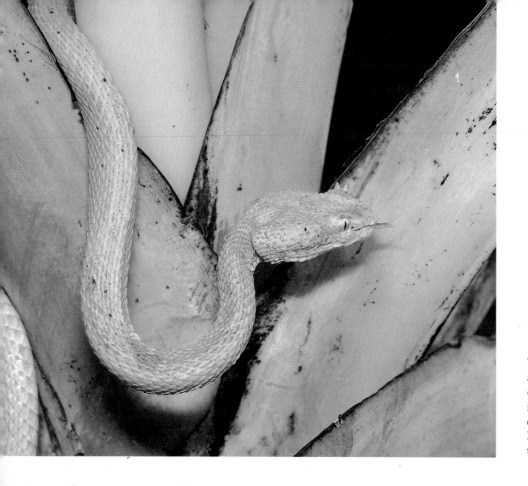

The golden eyelash viper (left) is a slim, agile snake, adapted to life in the tree tops of Central American rain forests. Sharing its island home with the famous Komodo dragon, the red-tailed pit viper (below) of Indonesia is actually more dangerous than the giant, carnivorous lizards.

A common hazard of the American West, the prairie rattlesnake (above) has a testy temper and a range that extends from western Iowa to the Rockies. It is most often found in grasslands, and will hunt prairie dogs through their burrows. The banded rock rattlesnake (below) is restricted to mountains in the Southwest; a small rattler, it rarely exceeds two feet in length.

The facial pit of this red diamondback rattlesnake is clearly visible between the nostril and eye; a heat-sensing organ, the pit allows the snake to hunt for rodents after dark. The forked tongue of the Mojave rattlesnake (below) is another sensory organ. Its venom has both hemotoxic and neurotoxic properties. *Opposite:* The black-tailed rattler is found near rock piles, cliffs, and ledges in the central plains of Texas. The rattlesnake's unique tail is thought to have evolved as a way of scaring off herds of horses, camels, and bison during the Pleistocene Epoch.

Index of Photography